Eggs with Legs

An Osprey's Story

Based on an idea by Lou Wyllie in celebration of the Year of the Osprey 2019
65 years residency in Strathspey and 60 years management by the RSPB

Written and illustrated by:

Finn Anderson, Olly March, Wiosna Wieczorek, Reuben O'Kane, Angus Cormack,

William Weir, Emily Millar, Archie Henderson, Danni McFadyen, Josie O'Kane,

Steven Millar, Dylan McFadyen, Saskia Sneddon, Finlay Henderson

With support from:
Alan Grieve, artist
Sarah Walker, RSPB Community Learning Officer
Jonathan Marshall, teacher

Front cover by Dylan McFadyen

All proceeds from the sale of this book go to the Year of the Osprey

First printed in the UK 2018 by Nancy Chambers Publishing

Copyright © 2018 by Deshar Pirmary School

ISBN: 978-1-9999233-2-7

Layout by Victoria Barlow

Printed in the UK by Groverprint & Design

Funded by Boat of Garten Community Company.
Scottish Company limited by guarantee (224956) Scottish Charity (SC032531)

PYLONS

One sunny day two eggs sat in a nest on top of an electric pylon.

Suddenly small cracks appeared
and two legs came out of one egg
and it started to run around the nest.

Then a jagged large crack appeared across both the eggs
and another crack and another until the eggs shattered
and out came two beautiful chicks one boy and one girl.

The mother and father had two beautiful osprey
chicks and their names were Eli and Nite.
The mother taught her chicks manners.

A few weeks later Eli and Nite
began flapping their wings.

They trained hard eating the fish
their parents brought and flapping
their wings until they both managed
to hover for a few seconds.

Very soon they were
strong and brave enough
to take off from the nest.

As soon as they could fly their
parents taught them how to fish,
but the first 20 times were fails.

Then on the 21st time
Eli caught a fish
and she felt amazing.

One dark midsummer night
after they had fallen asleep
their parents left for Africa
and Eli and Nite were all alone.

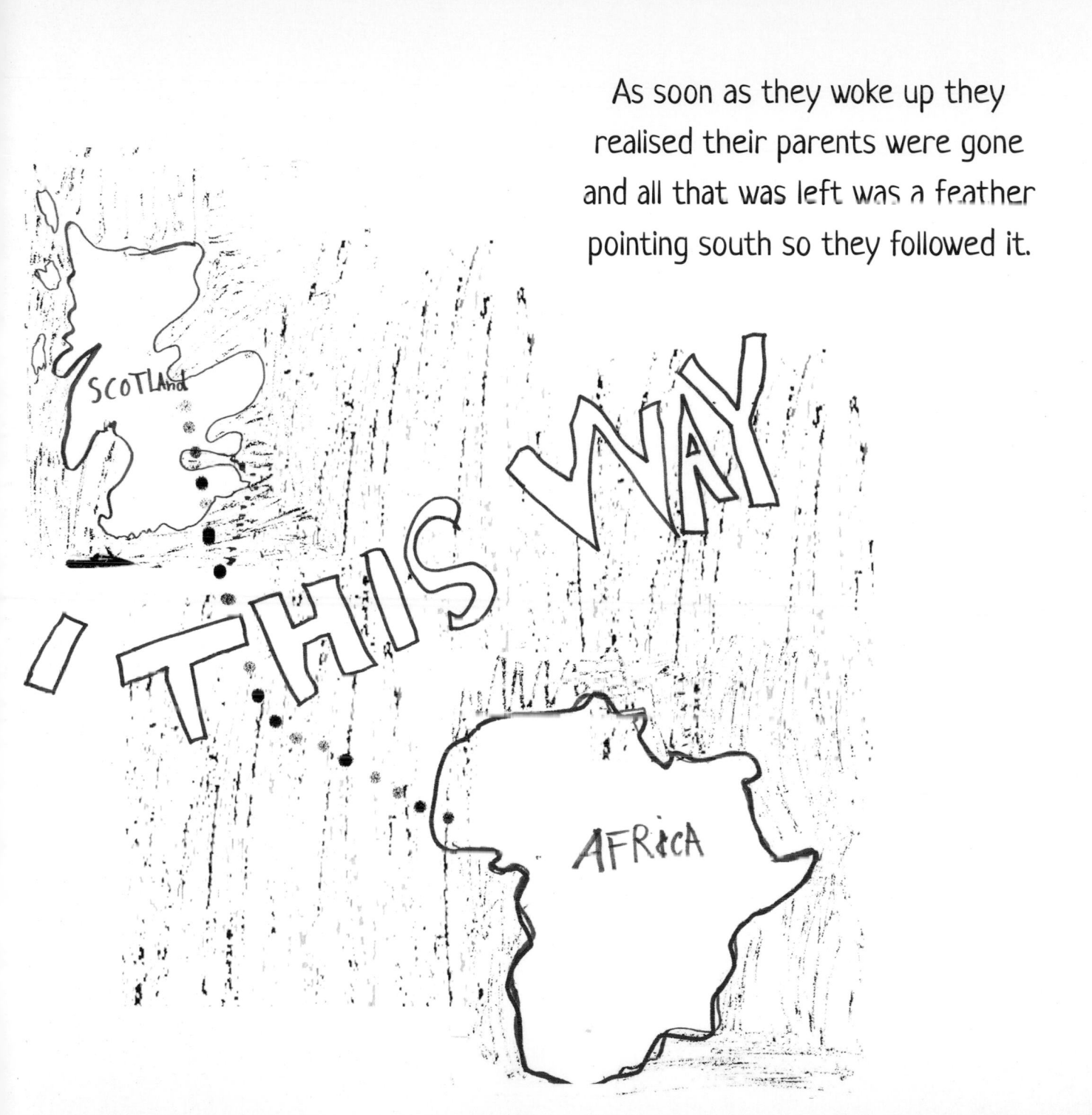

As soon as they woke up they realised their parents were gone and all that was left was a feather pointing south so they followed it.

On the way Eli flew through a rainbow and her entire body was all the colours of the rainbow.

The tip of Nite's wing turned colourful and he was horrified but Eli was delighted with her beautiful feathers.

The weather grew stormy and Eli was not happy
for very long because she got so tired and both
the ospreys started losing altitude.

With one of his amazing eyes
Nite spotted an island and it was
the perfect place to rest.

So down they swooped and landed,
but as soon as their claws touched
the ground a huge spout of water
came up out of the island and soaked
them washing the rainbow colours off.

Then it seemed the island spoke
and a deep voice and said

**"I am not an island but you
will find land over there."**

Surprised and thankful they went the way the whale had gestured with his tail and soon found Africa.

As they flew they saw all sorts of strange weird and funny animals.

AfricA

After flying a great distance and
marvelling at what they had seen
they decided to rest in a big tall tree.

They were so tired they fell asleep
and didn't even notice when other
birds landed on it.

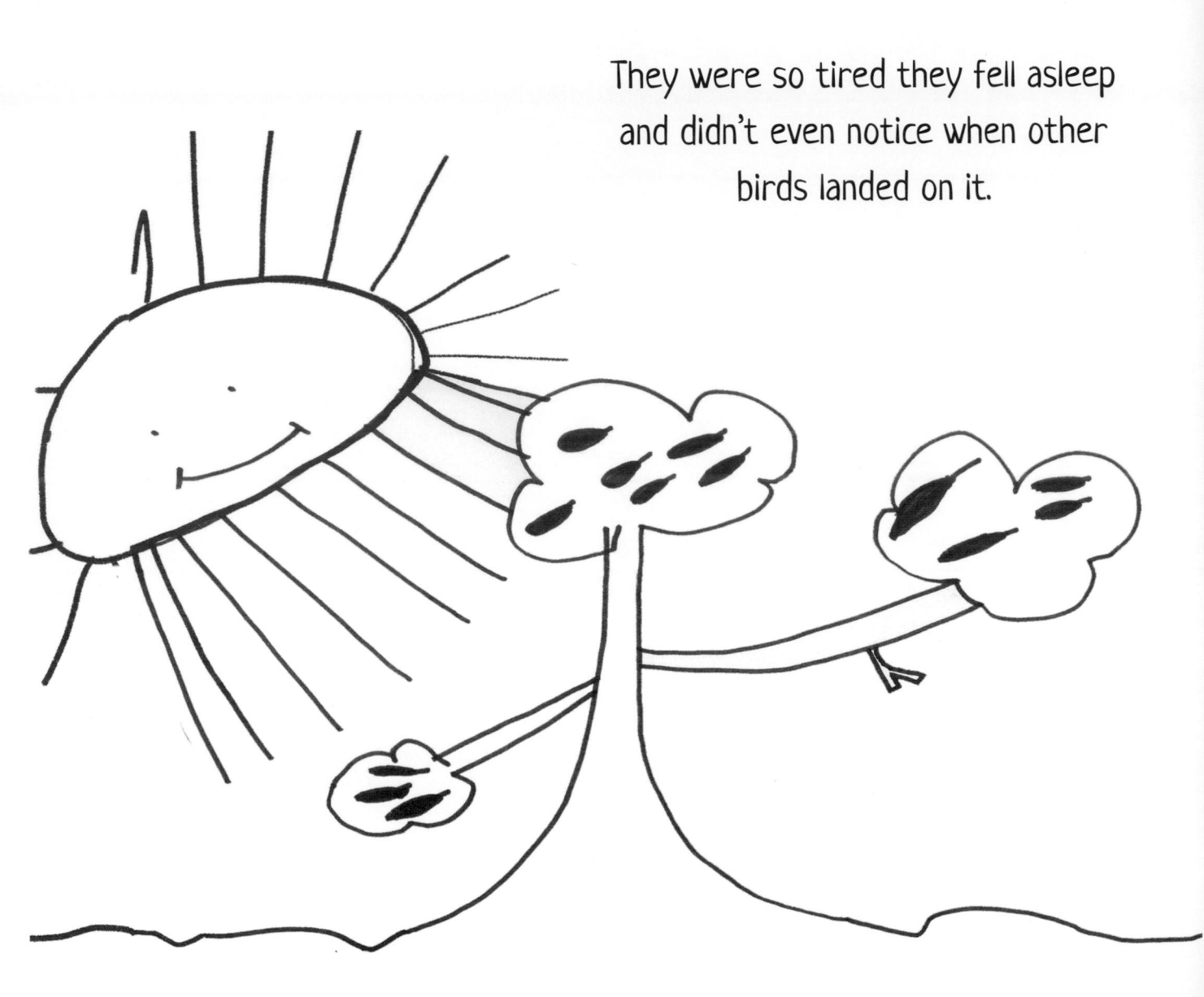

Then the next day they woke
to find that their Mum and Dad
were on either side of them.

THE END